Gunther von Hagens'

BODY WORLDS

The Original

& The Cycle of Life

Angelina Whalley

TABLE OF CONTENTS

The Cycle of Life   5

It Starts with a Single Cell   6

Why Do We Age?   9

The Mathematics of Life   10

The Silent Witness   12

Fit as a Fiddle   15

You Can't Teach an Old Dog New Tricks   16

A Long Goodbye   19

When Your Arms Get Too Short   22

The Artist's Gaze   24

Battle the Radicals   26

Up in Smoke   28

A Lifelong Struggle   30

Under Pressure   32

The Constricted Heart   35

You Are What You Eat   36

Too Much of a Good Thing   38

Hairy Times   40

Waves of Lust   44

Beyond Post-Reproductive Prime   46

Sexy Sixties   48

Masters of the Art of Ageing   50

When the Heart Won't Go On   60

Publishing Information   64

*Y*our body is the harp of your soul.
And it is yours to bring forth
sweet music from it
or confused sounds.

Khalil Gibran (1883-1931)
Lebanese American artist,
poet and writer

The Cycle of Life

The human body.
A marvel of contradictions.
Simple yet complex.
Vulnerable yet resilient.

Our bodies will be with us throughout our lives,
to help us experience ourselves and the world around us.
They show us the limits of our experience,
yet represent the starting point
of our boundless potential.

Nevertheless, our bodies are
not only a divine gift or bounty of nature.
They are also our very own personal responsibility,
the sum total of our lifestyle.

Good health is a highly fragile condition.

From conception to birth
and from infancy to childhood,
from adolescence to youth
and from adulthood to old age –
the only thing that remains throughout is constant change.

The human body – a lifelong challenge
and a visible reflection of our human clock.

It Starts with a Single Cell

Life begins with a single cell, or zygote,
after the father's sperm
fertilises the mother's egg.

The zygote contains the human genome,
the individual blueprint of a human being.
It consists of the parents' gene pairs,
organised in chromosomes.

This special set of chromosomes,
which has never existed before
and will never be recreated,
determines the characteristics and traits
of the conceived human being.

The zygote is hardworking and tireless.
About 30 hours after conception,
it begins to divide
and starts travelling down the Fallopian tube.
On its way it continues to divide into multiple cells.
On the sixth day after conception,
it attaches to the wall of the uterus.

After approximately 266 days,
a new human being enters the stage of life.

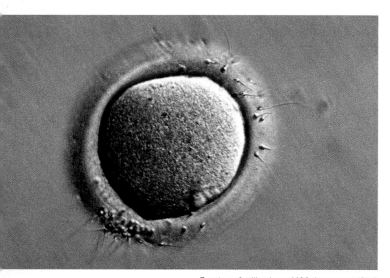

Zygote or fertilised egg (400 times magnified).

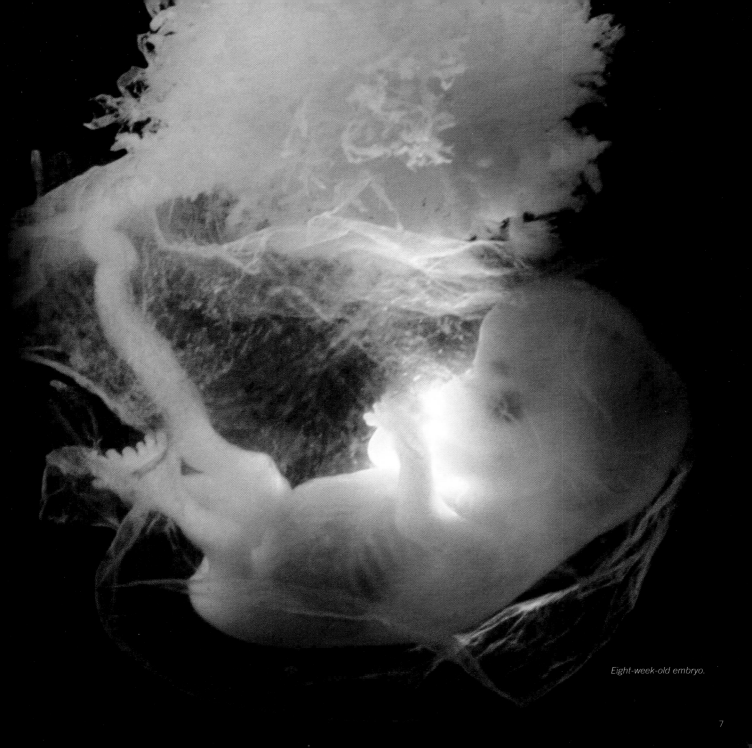

Eight-week-old embryo.

$\mathcal{L}$ife is the only art
    that we are required to practise without preparation,
    and without being allowed the preliminary trials,
    the failures and botches, that are essential
    for the training of a mere beginner.

Lewis Mumford (1895-1990)
American historian

Why Do We Age?

Ageing is not a sudden event,
but raher a gradual biological process.
It begins at birth,
and progresses inexorably through life,
ending at death.

From the moment of birth,
our physical efficiency increases
and reaches its peak in our mid-twenties.
From then on, it declines continuously.

Expressed simply,
our cells lose their resilience,
causing organ functions to weaken.

This is manifested in
increased susceptibility to infections,
lower hormone production,
weakened connective tissue
and poorer memory retention.

The causes of ageing are complex,
and have by no means been fully investigated.

One reason for ageing is that our cells
cannot divide and renew themselves
an unlimited number of times.

The chromosomes shorten
with each cell division,
until the death of the cell is inevitable.

The body's self-repairing processes
also decline with advancing age.

So-called free radicals
play a special part in the ageing process.
These extremely aggressive oxygenic molecules
develop in the body
as by-products of the metabolism
and cause the body to "rust" from the inside out.

We cannot halt or reverse the ageing process.
But the extent of age-related change
varies dramatically from person to person.

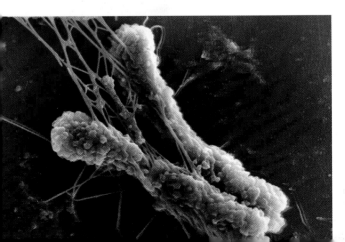

Stereoscopic image of a chromosome. A chromosome is formed
from a single DNA molecule that contains many genes.

The Mathematics of Life

Life spans of animal species differ considerably,
and seem to correlate with their heartbeat.
Most mammals have a fixed potential number
of heartbeats in their lifespan – around a billion.

A shrew, for instance, lives life in the fast lane.
Its heart skips along at 1,000 beats a minute,
using up all its heartbeats in less than four years.

A larger animal, with a lower metabolic rate,
breathes more slowly and has a slower heart rate.
For example, an elephant's heart pumps
a leisurely 30 times a minute.
Elephants can live for up to 70 years.

As a rule, larger animals
reach sexual maturity later
and live longer than smaller ones.

The life expectancy of animals also depends
on their environment, their food supply,
and whether or not they live in captivity.

Compared to other mammals of similar size,
the human lifespan,
which can be more than 100 years,
is unusually long.

We grow very slowly,
mature sexually much later,
and often live many decades
beyond our reproductive years.

One billion heartbeats would last
a human about 27 years.
However, we have managed
to more than double our life expectancy
by conquering famine and disease
and adjusting to our environments.

The shrew lives less than four years.

The Silent Witness

Like no other organ,
the skin bears witness
to our journey through time.

The supple luminescence of childhood
gives way to skin eruptions in adolescence.
The smooth complexion of youth is marked
by wrinkles and lines in later years.
Telltale scars record our mishaps and battles.

In our twenties,
the production of collagen decreases,
the protein that gives firmness,
strength and resilience to skin.
Elastin, the key to supple skin and flexibility,
also declines.

As we mature, skin loses its plumpness
and smoothness
to become thin and transparent,
and wrinkles begin to appear.
The loss of fat under the skin results in
hollowing of the cheeks and eye sockets.

While these effects are likely to happen to all of us,
the speed at and extent to which our skin ages
is only partly influenced by genetic factors.
Far more significant influences on ageing
are lifestyle factors.

UVA rays from sun exposure
break down the collagen and elastin in our skin.
They also induce sun spots or age spots.

Smoking wrinkles the skin
and gives it a slightly grey complexion,
resulting from poor circulation.

The effects of stress and lack of sleep
may easily show on the skin:
dryness, sensitivity, spots, and excess oil.
Getting enough sleep is important,
as it is during sleep that our bodies and skin
have time to repair and rejuvenate.

The health of our skin
plays a huge part in how old we feel,
and is the most visible indicator
of our age to others.

True life is lived when tiny changes oc...

$\mathcal{D}$on't part with your illusions.
When they are gone
you may still exist,
but you have ceased to live.

Mark Twain (1835-1910)
American humorist, lecturer, and writer

Fit as a Fiddle

The complex scaffolding of muscles and bones
allows us to achieve remarkable feats
of coordination and balance,
and keeps us moving throughout our lives.

Most mammals can walk
within hours or days of birth.
Humans take 6 to 12 months
just to master the basics.

Youth through adulthood is a time
of adventure, physical recklessness,
and peak performance.
Our bones are flexible,
hard to break, and quick to heal.

In adulthood, the body increases
in strength and stamina but loses flexibility.

With increasing age
our locomotive system changes:

- The calcium content in our bones decreases;
  they become less resilient and more brittle.

- Cartilage in the joints starts to wear out.

- The ligaments lose elasticity
  which limits mobility.

- Muscle fibres atrophy,
  to be replaced by fat and connective tissue,
  thus diminishing our strength.

But physical decline varies in individuals.
With training, the body can remain efficient
into our seventies.

Regular exercise has multiple benefits.
It strengthens muscles and bones,
reduces fat deposits,
stimulates the brain,
and helps the immune system
protect the entire body
against disease and the effects of ageing
on a long-term basis.

You Can't Teach an Old Dog New Tricks

Not true.
Even though learning becomes harder in old age.

For a long time it was thought
that the brain stopped developing after puberty
and started to decline.

In fact, throughout the course of our lives
numerous nerve cells die and the brain shrinks.
It produces fewer chemical messengers
(neurotransmitters)
and information is processed more slowly.

For this reason, learning
takes progressively longer,
and lessons must be repeated more often.
However, the brain remains flexible
and versatile throughout our lifetime.
It can grow new cells and build new neural networks.
This ability to restructure cells
is fundamental to a sound learning process.

Slower learning ability in old age
is often due to lack of:

- mental exercise,
- sensory stimulation, and
- physical exercise of gross and fine motor skills.

From birth to old age,
our mental faculties depend on our readiness
to take every opportunity to think harder
and to learn new things.

Use it or lose it!

The elderly have played an important role
throughout history
as a source of knowledge, experience, and wisdom.

More and more people
reach an advanced age,
and they represent a vital resource: knowledge.

Their ability to think analytically and laterally,
their empathy, conscientiousness,
and self-assertion
all give them a head start
and not just at work.
It's no accident that older people
often hold leading positions.

There are many impressive examples:

Leopold Stokowski,
one of the most famous conductors
of the 20th century and of Polish American origin,
was appointed director of the London Symphony
Orchestra at the age of 90.
He continued to work up until a few months
before his death at age 95.

Leopold Stokowski
(1882-1977)

Johann Wolfgang von Goethe
(1749-1832)

Johann Wolfgang von Goethe,
the famous German poet,
completed the second part
of his most famous work,
Faust, aged 82.

Emmanuel Kant,
the well-known German philosopher,
published his greatest works,
valued by successive generations to this day,
between the ages of 60 and 80.

Emmanuel Kant
(1724-1804)

*W*e stay young
as long as we keep learning,
acquire new habits,
and tolerate disagreement.

Marie von Ebner-Eschenbach (1830-1916)

Austrian writer

A Long Goodbye

The word 'dementia' is used to describe
a collection of symptoms
including a decline in memory,
reasoning and communication skills,
and a gradual loss in the ability to carry out
daily activities including personal care.

These symptoms are caused
by structural and chemical changes in the brain.

Diagnosis can be difficult, as early signs
could also be attributed to stress or depression.

Alzheimer's disease is the most common form
of dementia.
During the course of the disease,
'plaques' and 'tangles' develop in the structure
of the brain, causing brain cells to die.

Dementia can affect people under 65
but is most common in older people.
One in six people over 80 live
with one form or another of dementia.

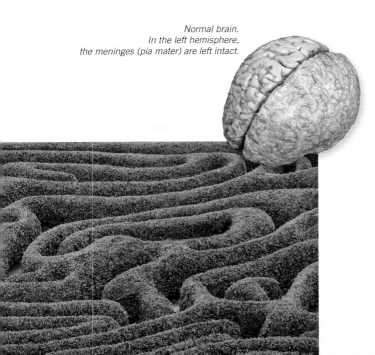

Normal brain.
In the left hemisphere,
the meninges (pia mater) are left intact.

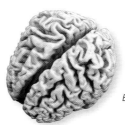

Brain with Alzheimer's disease.

Alzheimer's disease is a progressive
and ultimately fatal brain disorder
in which brain cells are gradually destroyed,
causing the cerebral cortex to atrophy.
The physical effects of the disease
can be seen here as the significant widening
of the grooves in the cortex.

"Journey into the sunset of my life"

Open letter by Ronald Reagan

On November 5, 1994, Ronald Reagan issued a letter to the American people, revealing that he had been diagnosed with Alzheimer's disease. His public announcement helped increase public awareness and reduce the social stigma associated with the deadly disease.

My fellow Americans,

I have recently been told that I am one of the millions of Americans who will be afflicted with Alzheimer's disease. Upon learning this news, Nancy and I had to decide whether as private citizens we would keep this a private matter or whether we would make this news known in a public way.

In the past, Nancy suffered from breast cancer and I had my cancer surgeries. We found through our open disclosures we were able to raise public awareness. We were happy that as a result, many more people underwent testing. They were treated in early stages and able to return to normal, healthy lives.

So now we feel it is important to share it with you. In opening our hearts, we hope this might promote greater awareness of this condition. Perhaps it will encourage a clearer understanding of the individuals and families who are affected by it.

At the moment I feel just fine. I intend to live the remainder of the years God gives me on this Earth doing the things I have always done. I will continue to share life's journey with my beloved Nancy and my family. I plan to enjoy the great outdoors and stay in touch with my friends and supporters.

Unfortunately, as Alzheimer's disease progresses, the family often bears a heavy burden. I only wish there was some way I could spare Nancy from this painful experience. When the time comes, I am confident that with your help she will face it with faith and courage.

In closing, let me thank you, the American people, for giving me the great honor of allowing me to serve as your president. When the Lord calls me home, whenever that day may be, I will leave with the greatest love for this country of ours and eternal optimism for its future.

I now begin the journey that will lead me into the sunset of my life.
I know that for America there will always be a bright dawn ahead.

Thank you, my friends. May God always bless you.

Sincerely,

Ronald Reagan

Ronald Reagan

$\mathcal{M}$y life was hurrying,

racing tragically toward its end.

And yet at the same time

it was dripping so slowly,

so very slowly now,

hour by hour, minute by minute.

Simone de Beauvoir (1908-1986)
French philosopher, writer, and feminist

When Your Arms Get Too Short

With increasing age
our ability to focus on nearby objects
declines noticeably.

While an infant
can focus right in front of his or her own nose,
a thirty-year-old must hold an object
about 15 centimetres (6 inches) away.

From their fifties on, most people
can read small print only at arm's length.
This is a normal result of ageing,
called presbyopia.

It develops because the lens
gradually loses its elasticity.
Often, the loss of elasticity is accompanied
by a clouding of the lens.
This is a cataract.

Sufferers perceive their surroundings
as increasingly blurred,
particularly in dim light,
and sensitivity to glare increases.

In serious cases the affected lens
can be replaced with an artificial one.

Other age-related eye conditions
are more serious,
and can lead to blindness.

Apart from cataracts,
some typical eye problems
developed by those over sixty include:

- Glaucoma, which increases
  internal pressure in the eyeball.

- Age-related macular degeneration
  that affects the cells of the retina.

- Long-term diabetes
  that can cause severe deterioration of the retina,
  leading to blindness.
  This can also affect younger people.

Often, these conditions cause discomfort
only after the eye has already
suffered permanent damage.

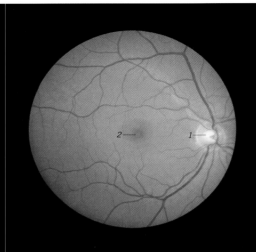

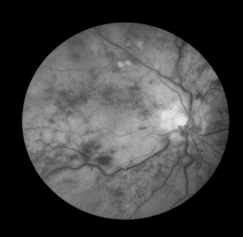

Normal interior surface of the eye (fundus)
with retina (1), optic disc and macula (2),
the point of sharpest focus within the eye.

Inflammation caused by diabetes
impedes blood circulation in the retina.
New blood vessels can form,
but with weaker walls.
They tend to bleed easily, leaving scars,
which may eventually cause blindness.

Poor eyesight or blindness
make life difficult.

When simple activities
such as reading, writing, driving, cooking,
and climbing stairs unaided
become impossible,
it is hard to lead an independent life.

For this reason we need to
protect our eyes from the sun,
eat healthily, especially fresh fruit and vegetables,
and get regular check-ups by an optician.

Better eyesight means a better life!

The Artist's Gaze

The Impressionist painters
Claude Monet (1840-1926)
and Edgar Degas (1834-1917)
are among the most recognised artists today.

Both had eye disease and failing vision
late in life, although they continued to paint.

These computer simulations
based on medical and historical knowledge
show how Degas and Monet saw the world
late in their careers, with failing vision.

Their eyesight may have affected their style.

We are grateful to Dr. Michael F. Marmor –
past Chair of the Department of Ophthalmology
at Stanford University, USA –
for his research, scholarship,
and interpretation in this presentation.

At the age of 72,
Monet was diagnosed with cataracts
which progressed over the next decade.
They not only blurred his vision,
but also made colours murky.

As his cataracts became dense,
Monet was aware of his broadening brushstrokes,
but he had trouble distinguishing
his paintings by colour.
He was painting by "labels of the tubes of paint"
and "force of habit".

During these years, Monet complained that colours
"no longer had the same intensity for me".

Records indicate that at the age of 82
Monet's vision in his better eye was 6/120 (20/200).
That is to say he could only perceive at six metres (20 feet)
what a normally-sighted person would be able to see
from a distance of 120 metres (200 feet).
He finally had cataract surgery in 1923.

Visual acuity can be measured by the distance
from which we can see objects clearly.

6/6 (20/20) is the standard,
meaning you can see all the letters
on the optician's chart clearly from 6 metres (20 feet) away.

What Monet painted:

The Japanese Bridge at Giverny.
Oil on canvas, 1918-1924.
Museé Marmottan, Paris.

What Monet probably saw:

At the time Monet painted the picture
his visual acuity was 6/120 (20/200).
This means he was only able to see objects
from a 6 metre (20 feet) distance that normal
sighted people would see from a 120 metre
(200 feet) distance.

"Ah! Sight! Sight! Sight!...
the difficulty of seeing makes me
feel numb."

Letter to friend, Evariste de Valernes
Paris, 6 July, 1891

Degas developed an age-related eye condition
that affected his focal point:
age-related macular degeneration.
The cells of the retina break down,
and eyesight in the centre of the field of vision
is reduced.

Degas' eyesight worsened over forty years.
His view of the world became increasingly blurred.
Outlines seemed smoother to him,
which may explain the style of his later paintings.

When Degas painted "Woman Drying Her Hair",
his eyesight had dropped to somewhere
around 6/130 (20/300).
After 1900 there was virtually no detail
in faces or clothing.

What Degas painted:

Woman Drying Her Hair,
Pastel on paper, 1905.
Norton Simon Art Foundation.

What Degas probably saw:

At the time Degas painted the picture,
his visual acuity was 6/130 (20/300),
meaning he could not have identified
the top letter on the optician's chart.

Battle the Radicals

Pollution, radiation, smoking,
and even breathing and energy production
in our cells create free radicals.

Free radicals are molecules
that are missing an electron,
thus becoming unstable.

They oxidise other molecules,
which in turn may become dysfunctional
and free radicals themselves,
creating a chain reaction.

The oxidative damage they cause
has been linked to ageing and many diseases,
such as cancer, Alzheimer's and arteriosclerosis.

However, the connection between free radicals
and accelerated ageing has been challenged,
as researchers find that free radicals
are only one part of the complex ageing process.

Oxygen and its by-products are corrosive. Every breath that brings life-giving oxygen to our cells, also ages us, because some oxygen molecules degrade into free radicals, rusting us from the inside.

We need a continuous supply of oxygen,
so our cells are continuously producing free radicals.

Alongside these are other environmental factors,
such as UV-light, radioactivity,
pesticides and cigarette smoke,
which add to the count of free radicals in our cells.

The body minimises the oxidative damage
with the help of antioxidants,
as they can neutralise free radicals
by donating electrons to them.

The list of antioxidants includes
vitamin C and E, beta-carotene,
and the trace element selenium.

They can be obtained naturally
from fruit and vegetables,
such as berries, grapes, nuts, beans,
broccoli, turmeric and cinnamon.

A balanced diet with plenty of fruit
and a little red wine
helps the body to fight off free radicals.

A vitamin-rich diet protects our body from free radicals.

Up in Smoke

smoker's lungs

non-smoker's lungs

Whether you chew it, smoke it, or sniff it,
tobacco is a thief.
It robs us of our health and quality of life,
and shortens our lives by several years.

Every child knows
that smoking causes the body serious damage;
it's even written on every cigarette packet.

But millions of people
still reach for a cigarette every day,
because the nicotine it contains
stimulates a mechanism in the brain
that prompts a sense of well-being and reward.

Smoking is not only a bad habit,
but also an addiction.
That's why it is so hard to give up.

But many people manage it, and it's worth it!
The health risks decrease gradually,
even after many years of tobacco consumption.

The inhaled nicotine reaches the brain
via the blood within seconds.
The breathing rate accelerates,
arteries narrow,
and heart rate and pulse increase rapidly.

Over time, smoking accelerates the ageing process,
weakens our immune system,
and increases the risk of contracting diseases,
such as cancer, heart disease, stroke,
eye disease, dementia, and Alzheimer's.

This doesn't only affect heavy smokers;
occasional smokers and passive smokers
have an increased risk of illness, too.

Studies show that 20% of all deaths
caused by heart disease are related to smoking.

However, abstaining from cigarettes for 5 years
has been shown to lower the risk of heart attack
to a level comparable to that of a non-smoker.

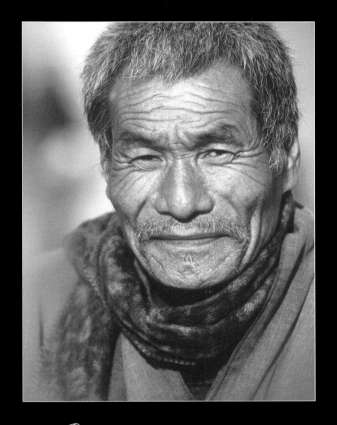

A man must have grown old and lived long
in order to see how short life is.

Arthur Schopenhauer (1788-1860)
German philosopher

A Lifelong Struggle

The immune system is the body's defence
against infectious organisms
and other invaders.

Organs work in concert, building barriers
to prevent hazardous matter from entering the body.
They also detect and neutralise organisms
that have broken those barriers.

Here are some signs that your immune system
is working, and the organs involved:

- A cut or bite becomes inflamed and itches (skin)

- You cough or sneeze (nose, lungs)

- You develop a fever (hypothalamus)

- Swellings appear in your neck, armpits, or groin
  (lymph glands)

- You feel nauseous or vomit (stomach)

- You get diarrhoea (intestines, bowel)

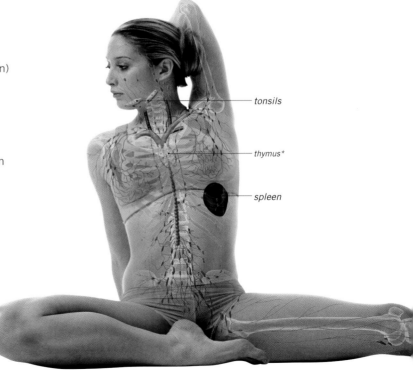

tonsils

thymus*

spleen

*The lymphatic system is composed of lymph vessels, lymph nodes, spleen, and thymus,
as well as the lymphoid follicles associated with the digestive system, such as the tonsils.
* Much of the thymus gland structure typically atrophies by age 20.*

A major component of the immune system
are our white blood cells – the leukocytes.
They are produced and stored in many locations
throughout the body, including the thymus, spleen,
bone marrow, and lymph nodes.

They circulate through the entire body
by means of lymphatic and blood vessels,
constantly monitoring for microorganisms
or other substances that might cause problems.

Some leukocytes, called phagocytes,
ingest and destroy invading organisms.
Others, known as B- and T-lymphocytes,
learn to remember and recognise
previous invaders by producing antibodies.

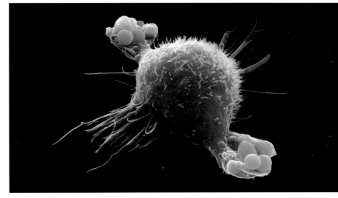

Phagocyte engulfing bacteria
as part of the immune system's response to infection
(9,000 times magnified).

As long as our immune system functions perfectly,
we are protected from most illnesses,
or can quickly recover from them,
ideally throughout our lives.

But the immune system can do more than that:
it can keep us young.

It protects the body
from self-produced substances,
such as acids and excess free radicals
that can damage our cells
and cause age-related illnesses and wrinkles.

A vitamin-rich diet, regular exercise,
plenty of sound sleep, and also laughter, fun and love,
all strengthen our immune system.

Under Pressure

Blood pressure is the force
the blood exerts against the blood vessel walls
when the heart pumps.
It rises with each heartbeat
and falls when the heart relaxes between beats.

Blood pressure is comprised of two values.
The higher, systolic number measures pressure
at the peak of each heartbeat.
The lower, diastolic number measures pressure
when the heart is resting between beats.

In an adult, normal blood pressure
is 120/80 mmHg when at rest.
It changes from minute to minute
and is affected by activity and rest,
emotions and temperature, diet and posture,
and medications.

High blood pressure or hypertension refers to
persistent blood pressure of 140/90 mmHg or higher.

Untreated hypertension affects all organ systems
and can shorten one's life expectancy
by 10 to 20 years,
for instance by increasing one's chance
of developing heart disease or a stroke.

In the last few decades,
the risk for high blood pressure has increased
because of a decline in healthy life styles.
In fact, nine out of ten people are at risk
for developing hypertension after age 50.

© Mike Baldwin / Cornered

"You've got the blood pressure of a
teenager – who lives on junk food, TV
and the computer."

*H*appiness is not something ready made.
It comes from your own actions.

*The 14th Dalai Lama (*1935)*

Head of state and spiritual leader
of the Tibetan people

*A*nyone who keeps the ability to see beauty
never grows old.

Franz Kafka (1883-1924)
Czech Austrian writer

The Constricted Heart

In a diseased artery,
a fatty substance called plaque
forms on the arterial walls.
The plaque may gradually become
a bulge that obstructs blood flow.

When a coronary artery is affected,
it causes angina, with symptoms such as
chest pains and shortness of breath.

More often, heart attacks result from plaque
that does not protrude into the artery itself,
but remains hidden in the artery wall.

During a heart attack,
the plaque suddenly ruptures,
causing a blood clot to form
that blocks the coronary artery.

Coronary artery disease appears to be
a lifelong process in some people,
beginning at an early age,
and progressing slowly.
It is often fatal because it remains undetected.

You Are What You Eat

Oil on canvas by Giuseppe Arcimboldo, around 1570.

... so the saying goes.
It couldn't be more true.
Research identifies a growing list of foods
that affect our health and well being,
and influence the way we age.

To stay healthy,
we need more than 40 different nutrients.
No single foodstuff can provide them all.

Research suggests that a diet
consisting of lots of fruits and vegetables,
olive oil, whole grains, legumes, fish,
and moderate amounts of red wine
promotes a longer life and reduces heart disease.

A healthy diet means
eat enough of everything,
and not too much of anything.

Obesity, with all its effects,
such as heart disease, arteriosclerosis,
diabetes, and joint pain,
reduces long term quality of life
and life expectancy.

Sugar in the form of simple, refined carbohydrates
is considered one of the major 'agers'.

Excess sugar molecules in the blood
attach to protein molecules,
thereby altering the structure
of the protein molecule.
As a result, the proteins cannot function properly,
leading to stiffening of body tissues.

The connective tissues
of the sinews, ligaments, and blood vessels
are particularly affected.

Although it is not yet proven
that a diet low in calories and high in nutrients
can lengthen human life, studies show
that people who consume considerably fewer calories
have less age-related decline in heart functions,
healthier arteries, and reduced DNA damage.

In later life, the body needs less energy.
From age thirty onwards,
the energy requirement decreases
by about eight percent per decade.

Fish is rich in Omega-3 fatty acids.
These acids are heart-protective, anti-inflammatory, and enhance brain functions.

Too Much of a Good Thing

Cholesterol is an essential building block of all body cells.
It is produced mainly in the liver
and ingested through various foods.

In order to reach the different regions of the body,
cholesterol attaches itself to certain proteins in the blood,
the so-called lipoproteins.

There are two kinds of lipoproteins:

- the low-density lipoproteins (LDL)

- and the high-density lipoproteins (HDL)

When doctors speak of "bad" cholesterol,
they mean the LDL cholesterol.
When too much of it accumulates in the artery walls,
white blood cells come to the rescue
as if the cholesterol were a foreign invader.
They engulf it and set off a chain of reactions
that result in the hardening and narrowing of arteries
and even their complete blockage
due to plaque formation.

"Good" HDL does the opposite.
It carries excess cholesterol out of the body's cells
and transports it back to the liver,
where it is broken down and discarded.

𝒯o know how to grow old
   is the master work of wisdom,
   and one of the most difficult chapters
   in the great art of living.

Henri Frédéric Amiel (1821-1881)
Swiss philosopher, poet, and critic

Hairy Times

When teenagers notice the first pimples flourishing,
when their voice deepens,
and beard, pubic, and axillary hair begin to sprout,
harmonious family life usually comes to an end.

Teens develop strange habits,
have sudden emotional outbursts,
and their interests seem incomprehensible.

During this phase of the cycle of life – puberty –
boys and girls become sexually mature.

It is caused by a complex fireworks of hormones.
It begins when the pituitary gland sends
a hormonal signal to the gonads
to increase the production of sex hormones.

In girls, it is primarily oestrogen,
and in boys, testosterone.
The sex hormones control
most physical changes during puberty.

Girls usually enter puberty
between age 8 and 13.
The first visible sign is the budding of breasts.
Pubic and axillary hair begin to grow.
Fat deposits give the hips and thighs a round shape.

About two years after the onset of puberty,
the first menstrual period – menarche – sets in.
However, the complex interplay
of the hormones involved is not yet synchronised,
often making the first monthly bleedings irregular.
With the first ovulation
girls become able to reproduce.

Boys enter puberty about two years later
than their female counterparts.
First the testicles and scrotum grow, then the penis.
By the age of 15,
most boys have had their first ejaculation.
At the same time, body hair and beard begin to grow,
and the scent-producing sweat glands develop.

Sex hormones also stimulate
rapid growth spurts during puberty.

Since boys enter puberty later than girls,
their growth phase is longer.
The final growth spurt is also more intense.
That explains why men
are on average 12 cm (5 inches) taller than women.

The extension of the vocal cords and
the growth of the larynx
cause the pubertal vocal changes.
Boys' voices deepen about an octave.

Essential reconstruction processes
also take place in the brain.
New neurons are formed,
and neural networks are re-established.
The changes in the frontal brain
cause the sudden and capricious behavior
which is the trademark of puberty.
This part of the brain is responsible
for judgment, planning, and risk assessment.

Puberty is a difficult time for adolescents, too.
They have to discover their bodies all over again
and accept its changes.
They take on new responsibilities
and begin to make decisions
which may affect the course of their lives.

$\mathcal{W}$e do not see things as they are;

we see things as we are.

The Talmud
Record of rabbinic discussions pertaining to Jewish law, ethics,
customs, and history

Waves of Lust

It is an equally indescribable
and overwhelming feeling
to be carried away by the waves of pleasure,
especially at the climax of love play.
But sexual ecstasy also serves
elementary biological purposes.

The urge to reproduce
is one of our strongest instincts.

The sensual pleasure during sex
is a constant incentive to connect physically.
In addition, in men
orgasm and reproduction are closely linked.

Physical love is an essential component
of our humanness
and guarantees the survival of our species.
This act of humanity is the source
of all our existence.

The anatomical bases of the sexual act
have long been puzzling and unclear.

Leonardo da Vinci made an early attempt
to illustrate the anatomy of the sexual act
at the end of the 15th century.

His drawing was strongly influenced
by the errors of his scientific predecessors
and by then-prevailing beliefs and worldviews.
It was therefore fundamentally flawed.

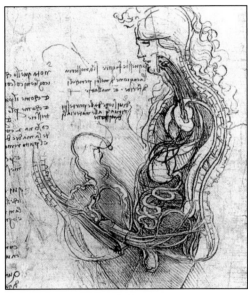

"The Copulation", around 1490.
As imagined and drawn by Leonardo da Vinci (1452-1519).

Since ancient times it was believed
that the male sperm was formed in the brain
and flowed through the spinal cord into the penis.
Heart and brain were regarded
as the place of spirit and soul.
Hence, the seeds for reproduction
naturally would have to originate in these organs.

It was also believed that the menstrual blood
that was absent during pregnancy
would be converted into milk in the breasts.
Scientists claimed the existence
of a blood vessel connecting the uterus and breasts.

In 1933,
New York obstetrician Robert Dickinson created
a more realistic representation of the sexual act.
He inserted a glass flask
in the size and shape of a penis
into the vagina of several test persons
and developed a better understanding
of the anatomy of sex.

Finally, modern imaging techniques
produced lifelike depictions of the sexual act
toward the end of the 1990s.
They could be created thanks to couples
who voluntarily climbed into the cramped space
of a magnetic resonance tomograph to make love.

A remarkable result of these studies was
that the penis can bend like a boomerang
inside the woman's body,
depending on the position of the couple.

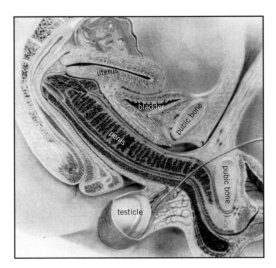

*Midsagittal image of the anatomy of sexual intercourse,
envisaged by R L Dickinson and drawn by R S Kendall, 1933.*

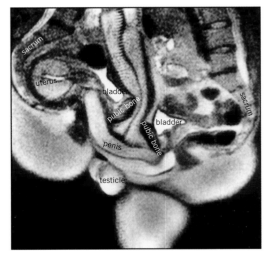

*Magnetic resonance imaging of male and female genitals
during coitus and female sexual arousal.*

Beyond Post-Reproductive Prime

As a woman's ovaries gradually produce
fewer fertile egg cells,
a chapter in her life story closes.
A period of transition begins,
called the change of life.

Her monthly periods become irregular,
and the production of oestrogen drops measurably,
until eventually no more eggs cells are being formed,
and bleeding ceases.
The very last bleeding is called the menopause.

The average age
at which women experience menopause is 52.

The change in hormone production
causes imbalances in many organ functions.
Hot flashes, depression, insomnia
and loss of bone density (osteoporosis)
are some of the side effects.

But this change in life is not an illness.
It is as natural a stage in a woman's life
as are puberty, pregnancy, and childbirth.

Not only women experience the change of life;
most men are also affected.

The most important male hormone is testosterone.
It stands for masculinity, strength, and aggression.

It also promotes bone density
and muscle development – in both men and women –
and helps break down fats,
reduce cholesterol levels, and synthesise proteins.

Testosterone levels decline in later life,
diminishing male sexual desire and libido.

However, most men do not lose their fertility.
Unlike women, they can reproduce in their later years.

An outward sign of reduced testosterone production
is declining beard growth.

Sexy Sixties

As our body changes
in middle and late adulthood,
so does our sexual activity.

This is generally associated
with reduced sexual desire, fewer erections,
and less intense orgasms.

Older men and women can enjoy intimacy
and experience a healthy sex life.
Studies show that staying sexually active
into our sixties, seventies, and eighties
has physical, social, and mental benefits.

Sex releases endorphins, relieves stress,
and fights depression and loneliness.

Research has shown
that regular orgasms may even increase
life expectancy by as much as eight years.

Generally our sexual desire
declines with increasing age,
we have fewer erections
and experience orgasm less frequently.

While it will take him longer to become erect,
he has better control over his ejaculation,
which may be a positive development
not only for him but also his partner.

While she may not lubricate as quickly,
she may enjoy the sex even more,
knowing that she no longer can get pregnant.

Sex is not only about performance,
but rather about sensory experiences
and nurturing relationships.

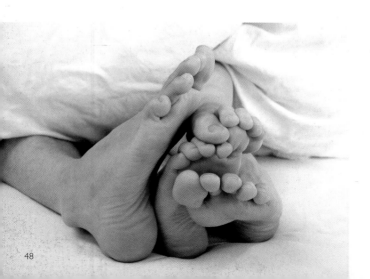

 *A*ge is an issue of mind over matter.
If you don't mind, it doesn't matter.

Mark Twain (1835-1910)
American humorist, lecturer, and writer

Masters of the Art of Ageing

They belong to a rarefied circle.
In a world of more than six billion,
there are only 450,000 of them.
They are centenarians –
the longest living people on earth.

Unlike their counterparts
in the developing world who succumb to disease
or endure old age, these elders are vital,
healthy, and youthful in body and mind.

Independent and active,
they are important participants in their families
and hold a special place in their communities.

There are several clusters
of exceptional centenarians in the world.
And it appears that these clusters
have much in common.

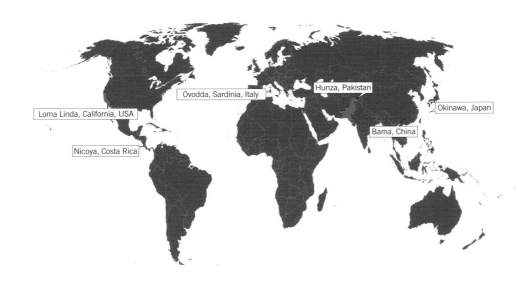

These six regions have been documented with unusually high populations of centenarians.

Less Is More

Their diets are traditionally low in meat and animal fat.
The elders of Okinawa, Japan, adhere to a principle called 'hara hachi bu' –
eating only until they are 80% full,
thus maintaining a daily intake of 1,900 calories.

Lifelong Learning
& Engaging with the World

Born in 1904, this woman has social and volunteer commitments,
attends exercise classes and learned to use a computer at age 101.
She is an active member of her church.

Eat a Rainbow

... containing lots of vegetables and fruits, fish and seaweed, soy and tofu, and red wine. A diet rich in vitamins, minerals, and antioxidants protects the super-agers against cancer, heart disease, and other ailments.

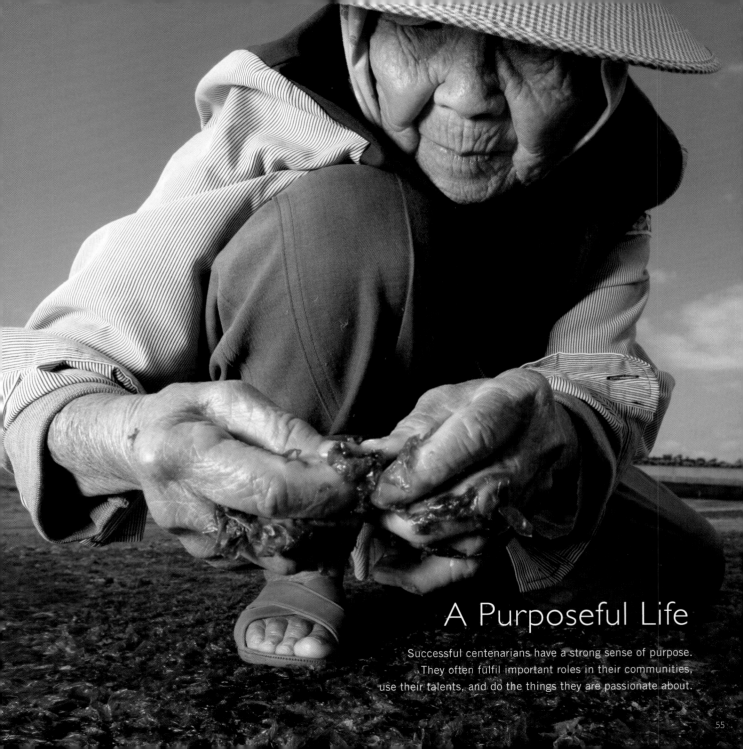

A Purposeful Life

Successful centenarians have a strong sense of purpose.
They often fulfil important roles in their communities,
use their talents, and do the things they are passionate about.

Exercise & Motion as a Way of Life

Centenarians stay fit by walking several miles a day, exercising regularly
or tending to their livestock and vegetable gardens.
For this 94 year old man, swimming is one of the ingredients
that make up quality of life.

Mean Something to Someone

The elders are often perceived as repositories of history and knowledge.
Friendships across the generational divide, with younger people and children,
boost their wellbeing.

The Curative Power of Nature

Taking a walk, praying, meditating, or having lunch with a friend
are stress-busting habits and sources of comfort and strength
to these super old citizens.

When the Heart Won't Go On

Death is not a sudden event,
but a process.

Death begins when the heart stops beating.
The supply of oxygen and nutrients
to the different regions of the body
is interrupted.

The cells start to die off
and organs cease to function.
First the brain is affected.

Diminishing brain activity
reduces consciousness and perception.

Respiration becomes shallower,
hearing and vision decline,
and finally its control over vital functions stops
completely.

The end of electrical activity in the brain –
brain death – is the legal definition
of the moment of death.

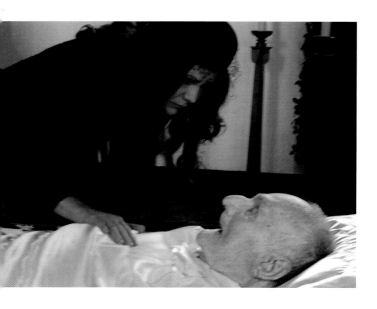

Ten to twenty minutes after brain death,
many of the cells in the heart start to die.

Next follows the death of the liver and lung cells.
Only one to two hours later
do the cells of the kidneys
finally cease to function.

Due to gravity, the blood in the body
drains from the capillaries and
sinks to the lower surfaces which grow darker,
while the upper surfaces
take on a paler hue.
Muscles gradually stiffen and
rigor mortis sets in.

The body loses its capacity
to fight off bacteria,
and cells quickly begin to die.
The cells' own enzymes and bacterial activity
cause the body to decompose,
at which time muscles lose their stiffness.

*G*et used to the idea that Death should not matter to us,

for good and evil are based on sensation.

Death, however, is the cessation of all sensation.

Hence, Death, ostensibly the most terrifying of all evils,

has no meaning for us,

for as long as we exist, Death will not be present.

When Death comes, then we will no longer be in existence.

Epikur (342-271)
Greek philosopher

$\mathscr{A}$nd in the end,

it's not the years in your life that count.

It's the life in your years.

Abraham Lincoln (1809-1865)
16th President of the United States of America

Publishing Information

Angelina Whalley
BODY WORLDS & The Cycle of Life

Design
www.die-werbeaktivisten.de, mArc schumacher, Weinheim

1st printing
© Copyright 2009

Arts & Sciences

Verlagsgesellschaft mbH, Heidelberg, Germany

Author:
A licenced physician, Angelina Whalley is the creative and conceptual designer of Gunther von Hagens' BODY WORLDS exhibition. She began her medical studies at Freie Universität in Berlin and then transferred to the University of Heidelberg, where she completed her doctorate in 1986. She also obtained her licence to practise medicine in the same year. She did scientific research at the Institute of Anatomy for three years, inter alia in the plastination laboratory, as well as at the Institute of Pahtology of the University of Heidelberg for two years. She has been the Director of the Institute for Plastination in Heidelberg since 1997. Since 1993, she has also been the Director of BIODUR® Products, a company that markets plastination formulas and auxiliaries worldwide.

ISBN 978-3-937256-13-9

www.bodyworlds.com